Mommy Says I Have Butterflies

May you and your butterflies have fun trying new things!

WRITTEN BY

Alice Walker

Alice Walker
2022

For Elizabeth,
Baba loves you
and your butterflies.

When I go to new places,
When I do new things,
When I meet new people …

I sometimes have tears, and it's hard to feel good.
Mommy says, "Elizabeth, you have butterflies,
and I sometimes get them too!"

The butterflies are in my tummy for a while;
but when I start having fun, they fly away.
I really like butterflies.
They are colorful and fly so gently.

They get their food from the flowers,
and I see them in the garden.

They don't really live in my tummy.
It's a thing people say when their tummy flutters
and feels jumpy.

I'm not sure I like that jumpy feeling in my tummy.
It always goes away when I start having fun!

Do you ever have jumpy feelings?

Mommy says lots of people have butterflies.
Mommy always understands my butterflies.
I asked my friends, and they said,
"We have butterflies too!"

Pretty soon …
When I'm with special friends,
my butterflies disappear!

My first time on the slide,
I didn't know what to expect.
The butterflies fluttered in my tummy.

I flew down the slide and laughed and giggled.

Pretty soon ...
My butterflies are having fun
on the slippery slide too!

Learning to ride my bike
for the first time
was something very new.

The bicycle and butterflies
would wiggle and wobble
as I tried to hold on.

Pretty soon ...
My butterflies are peddling fast too!

My first day of school,
I didn't know what it would be like.

The butterflies fluttered in my tummy.
There were things to do,
new friends to meet, and a nice teacher.

Pretty soon …
My butterflies are enjoying school,
especially recess!

One day at the playground,
there was a new little girl.

It looked like she had butterflies too.
I said, "Hello," and she smiled.

We played all afternoon
and had so much fun.

Pretty soon …
Our butterflies are climbing on the jungle gym!

My first time at the riding stable,
the horse seemed so big.

The butterflies fluttered in my tummy.

The handler led us around the corral.
The horse was gentle and riding was so much fun.

Pretty soon …
My butterflies are galloping into the field!

Sometimes, I get butterflies when I play the violin.
I had many butterflies the night of my violin recital.
I practiced,
knew the music,
and started to play.

Pretty soon ...
My butterflies are flying away
like notes into the air.

Going on the swings at the amusement park
is so much fun.

The swings at the amusement park seemed to go so high.
I felt butterflies when the ride began.
It went around and around very fast.

Pretty soon …
My butterflies are loving the ride and feeling free
… Just like me!

I have decided that it's okay to have butterflies.

Everyone has butterflies at different times.
Lots of people I love have butterflies.

I have also decided that butterflies like being free.
They don't want to be in my tummy.
They are happy when they can fly and play in the garden.

I'm older now,
and still get that jumpy, butterfly feeling sometimes.

It's okay to feel that way whatever your age!

Did you know?
Many people
around the world get
butterflies when
they have a
new experience.

Tell me about times
when you get butterflies in
your tummy.

Tell me how you feel when they fly away.

I like riding my bicycle fast on mountain trails.

I like performing in dance recitals.

I like acting in school plays and going to the theater.

I like trying new things and challenging myself.

I hope you will try new things too!

Did you know ...
Butterflies are not just a feeling you have in your tummy?

In fact ...
Butterflies are insects with four wings
that are often brightly colored with fun patterns.

There are so many different butterflies;
it's hard to count them all.
The butterfly life cycle has four stages ...

The butterfly life cycle...

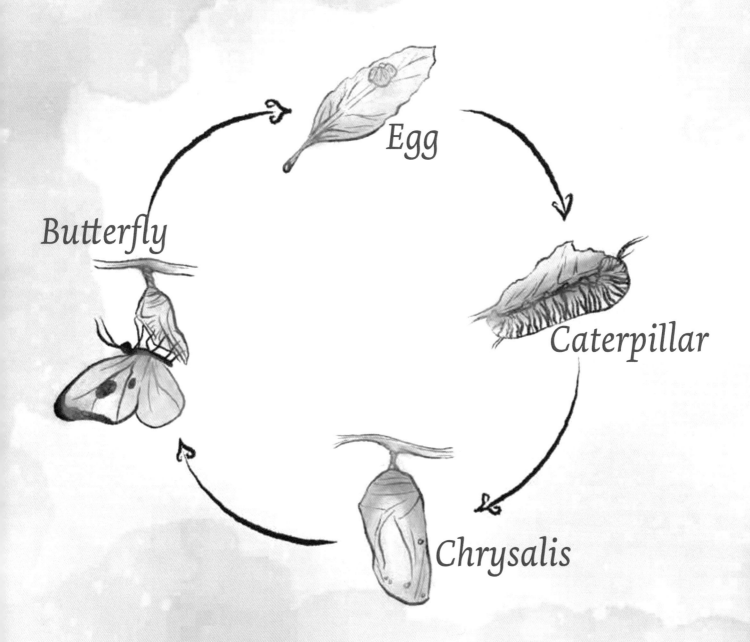

Egg

Caterpillar

Chrysalis

Butterfly

Egg — The butterfly begins life as a tiny egg that is laid on a plant leaf or stem. The egg gets nibbled open, and out comes a ...

Caterpillar (larva) — The caterpillar hatches from the egg and begins eating. It eats a lot, grows quickly, and sheds its skin many times. When the caterpillar is done growing, it spins silk so it can attach to a twig or leaf and begin forming a ...

Chrysalis (pupa) — The chrysalis is a busy place where the caterpillar body starts changing into a butterfly. After a time, the chrysalis slowly opens and out comes a ...

Butterfly — The butterfly wings get filled with a fluid that must first dry before it can fly. Butterflies live a week or more. They feed on the sweet nectar from flowers and move pollen between flowers. Butterflies fly, drink nectar, pollinate flowers, mate, and lay eggs for the lifecycle to begin again.

Let's make some beautiful butterflies!

You will need a piece of paper.
Then, crayons, colored pencils, markers, or paints.

The butterflies can be big and little.
They can fly in all directions.
They can have many colors.

Have fun!

Step 1:
Draw the body

Step 2:
Draw the larger top wings

Step 3:
Draw the smaller bottom wings

Step 4:
Have fun coloring!

About the Author

Alice Celia Martowski Walker grew up in Ludlow, MA. She has lived in many U.S. cities with her husband Charlie and their two daughters, Michele and Vanessa. Alice and Charlie are now retired in Chicago, IL. Alice enjoys volunteering, many artistic pursuits, gardening, long walks, and time with family.

The original story was written when her granddaughter Elizabeth was five years old. Elizabeth, now thirteen, loves the story and recently exclaimed ... "I think you should publish a book because other kids have butterflies too!" She is Alice's love and inspiration!

Elizabeth and Alice hope that children and adults reading this story will know that it's okay to have butterflies!

"A special thank you to my family
for their faithful support and cheerleading."

ISBN: 978-1-955622-63-9 (hardcover)
978-1-955622-62-2 (paperback)

Creative Director: Joanne Boufis
Creative Team: Paige DeBoer and Natalia Logvanova
Illustrations by: Katie Williams and Ferlina Gunawan

Published by JoFactor Entertainment, LLC
www.JoFactor.com